SERIES EDITOR: BRIAN SEAGER

OCR GCSE MATHEMATICS

STAGE

6

GRADUATED ASSESSMENT

SECOND EDITION

- Howard Baxter
- Michael Handbury
- John Jeskins
- Jean Matthews
- Mark Patmore

Hodder Murray
www.hoddereducation.co.uk

Hodder Headline's policy is to use papers that are natural, renewable and recyclable products and made from wood grown in sustainable forests. The logging and manufacturing processes are expected to conform to the environmental regulations of the country of origin.

Orders: please contact Bookpoint Ltd, 130 Milton Park, Abingdon, Oxon OX14 4SB. Telephone: (44) 01235 827720. Fax: (44) 01235 400454. Lines are open 9 a.m. to 5 p.m., Monday to Saturday, with a 24-hour message-answering service. Visit our website at www.hoddereducation.co.uk.

© Howard Baxter, Michael Handbury, John Jeskins, Jean Matthews, Mark Patmore, Brian Seager, Eddie Wilde, 2006
First published in 2006 by
Hodder Murray, an imprint of Hodder Education,
a member of the Hodder Headline Group
338 Euston Road
London NW1 3BH

Impression number   10 9 8 7 6 5 4 3 2 1
Year   2011   2010   2009   2008   2007   2006

Cover photo © Andy Sacks/Photographer's Choice/Getty Images
Typeset in 12pt Times Ten Roman by Tech-Set Ltd. Gateshead, Tyne and Wear.
Printed in Great Britain by CPI Bath

A catalogue record for this title is available from the British Library

ISBN-10: 0340 927 550
ISBN-13: 978 0340 927 557

Contents

STAG
6

Introduction

This book contains exercises designed to be used with the Graduated Assessment for OCR GCSE Mathematics course. The work covers Stage 6 of the specification.

Each exercise matches an exercise in the Graduated Assessment for OCR GCSE Mathematics Stage 6 Student's Book. The exercises in the textbook are numbered through each chapter. For instance, in Chapter 16, Exercise 16.2 is on drawing the graphs of straight lines with harder equations. The corresponding homework exercise is Exercise 16.2H.

You will find that the homework exercises are generally shorter than those in the Student's Book but still cover the same mathematics. Some questions are intended to be completed without a calculator, just as in the Student's Book. These are shown with a non-calculator icon in the same way. Doing these questions without a calculator is vital practice for the non-calculator sections of the module test and the GCSE examination papers.

The Homework Book gives you the opportunity for further practice on the work undertaken in class. It is also a smaller book to carry home! If you have understood the topics, you should be able to tackle these exercises confidently as they are no harder than the ones you have done in class.

More practice helps to reinforce the ideas you have learned and makes them easier to remember at a later stage. If, however, you do forget, further help is at hand. As well as the textbook, there is also, with this book, a Personal Tutor CD-ROM. This contains worked examples on key topics to revise concepts you find difficult and consolidate your understanding. The exercises supported with examples on the Personal Tutor CD-ROM are marked with an icon.

Using a calculator effectively

You may find the example useful for Exercises 1.1H and 1.2H.

EXERCISE 1.1H

Work out these, without a calculator.

1 a) $3 \times 5 + 6$ **b)** $2 \times (7 + 3)$

   c) $3 + 9 \times 2$ **d)** 4×5^2

2 a) $18 - 3 \times 5$ **b)** $(11 - 7) \times 5$

   c) 3×2^3 **d)** $(2 \times 4)^2$

3 a) $3 + \dfrac{10}{2}$ **b)** $\dfrac{9 + 5}{2}$

   c) $\dfrac{20}{4 \times 5}$ **d)** $\dfrac{20}{4} \times 2$

4 a) $\dfrac{8 + 4}{3} - 2$ **b)** $\dfrac{30}{5 + 1}$

   c) $\dfrac{20}{10} + 4$ **d)** $3 \times 9 - \dfrac{6 \times 2}{3}$

5 a) $(10 - 2 \times 3)^2$ **b)** $10 - 5 \times 3$

   c) $2 \times 4 - 8 \times 5$ **d)** $(5 + 4) \times (8 - 3)$

Use a calculator to work out these.

6 $15\cdot6 + 4 \times 3$ **7** $127\cdot1 - 5\cdot6 \times 15\cdot1$

8 $16\cdot4 - 3\cdot7 \times 2\cdot1$ **9** $18 - 2\cdot3 \times 5$

10 $7\cdot2 + 5\cdot1 \times 3\cdot4$

AGE
6

EXERCISE 1.2H

Use a calculator to work out these.

Give your answers either exactly or to 2 decimal places.

1 $^-2{\cdot}7 + 3{\cdot}8 - 4{\cdot}9 + 2{\cdot}1$ **2** $(^-2{\cdot}1 \times 4{\cdot}2) + (2{\cdot}7 \times {}^-4{\cdot}6)$

3 $\dfrac{4{\cdot}6 - 3{\cdot}7}{9 - 7{\cdot}4}$ **4** $\dfrac{^-2{\cdot}7 \times 3{\cdot}9}{2{\cdot}6 + 3{\cdot}7}$

5 $\dfrac{9{\cdot}2}{1{\cdot}3 + 5{\cdot}4}$ **6** $\dfrac{18{\cdot}4 - 9{\cdot}1}{3{\cdot}8}$

7 $\dfrac{10}{0{\cdot}56 - 0{\cdot}32}$ **8** $\dfrac{6{\cdot}7 + 9{\cdot}3}{8{\cdot}4 \times 4{\cdot}9}$

9 $(43{\cdot}7 - 18{\cdot}4) \div 3{\cdot}6$ **10** $\dfrac{16{\cdot}7 \times 5{\cdot}2}{6{\cdot}1 \times 0{\cdot}36}$

EXERCISE 1.3H

Work out these on your calculator without writing down the answers to the middle stages.

If the answers are not exact, give them correct to 3 decimal places.

1 $3{\cdot}2^4$ **2** $\sqrt{2^2 - 1{\cdot}8^2}$

3 $2{\cdot}3 \times 4{\cdot}7^2 - 4{\cdot}6 \div 2{\cdot}89$ **4** $\sqrt{17{\cdot}3 + 16{\cdot}8}$

5 $\sqrt{68{\cdot}7 - 2{\cdot}3^2}$ **6** $(7{\cdot}3 - 2{\cdot}6)^2$

7 $7{\cdot}3^2 - 2{\cdot}6^2$ **8** $5{\cdot}8 \times (1{\cdot}9 + 7{\cdot}3)^2$

9 $\sqrt{28{\cdot}6 - 9{\cdot}7}$ **10** $\sqrt{\dfrac{26{\cdot}2}{3{\cdot}8}}$

EXERCISE 1.4H

Do not use your calculator for questions **1** and **2**.

1 Write down the reciprocal of each of these numbers.

  a) 7   **b)** 12   **c)** 90   **d)** 100   **e)** 16

2 Write down the numbers of which these are the reciprocals.

  a) $\frac{1}{5}$ **b)** $\frac{1}{18}$ **c)** $\frac{1}{200}$ **d)** $\frac{1}{72}$ **d)** $\frac{1}{27}$

You may use your calculator for questions **3** and **4**.

3 Calculate the reciprocal of each of these numbers, giving your answer as a decimal.

  a) 2   **b)** 5   **c)** 1·6   **d)** 0·1   **e)** 25

4 Work out the reciprocal of each of these. Give your answers as fractions or mixed numbers.

  a) $\frac{3}{4}$ **b)** $\frac{2}{5}$ **c)** $\frac{5}{8}$ **d)** $2\frac{2}{5}$ **e)** $1\frac{2}{3}$

EXERCISE 1.5H

1 Find the total length of four pieces of string of these lengths.

    3 m 14 cm   5 m 27 cm
    2 m 89 cm   3 m 14 cm

2 Find the total weight of four sacks of parcels of these weights.

    5 kg 500 g   17 kg 314 g
    29 kg 863 g   9 kg 744 g

3 Here are the times that Mrs Long had to wait in the queue at the post office on her last four visits.

    4 minutes 15 seconds   9 minutes 12 seconds
    8 minutes 54 seconds   16 minutes 23 seconds

Find the total time that she waited.

4 Find the mean of these five lengths.

  3 km 200 m   3 km 190 m   2 km 846 m
  2 km 641 m   3 km 123 m

5 Jenny buys items weighing 568 g, 2·413 kg, 1·602 kg and 374 g. How much do they weigh altogether?
Give your answer in kilograms and grams.

6 In a four-part endurance race, a driver takes the following times to complete each part of the race.

  5 hours 38 minutes   6 hours 57 minutes
  5 hours 19 minutes   5 hours 46 minutes

What was the driver's total time for the race?
Give your answer in hours and minutes.

7 Convert these times to hours.

  a) 3 hours 30 minutes   **b)** 4 hours 15 minutes
  c) 1 hour 42 minutes   **d)** 2 hours 24 minutes

8 Write these times in minutes and seconds.

  a) 6·2 minutes   **b)** 14·75 minutes
  c) 8·8 minutes   **d)** 0·9 minutes

||||| EXERCISE 1.6H

Write down sensible values for each of these measurements.

1 The length of a garden is 17·284 m.

2 A baby weighs 3 kg 276 g.

Work out these and give the answers to a sensible degree of accuracy.

3 The length of a side of a square table with area 1·7 m².

4 The extra money Joanna receives when her wage of £58·40 is increased by 2·4%.

5 The average height of three people whose heights are 1·86 m, 1·63 m and 1·78 m.

6 The amount each person gets when £106 is shared between seven people.

AGE
5

Brackets and factors

EXERCISE 2.1H

Expand these brackets.

1 $7(3a + 6b)$ **2** $5(2c + 3d)$

3 $4(3e - 5f)$ **4** $3(7g - 2h)$

5 $3(4i + 2j - 3k)$ **6** $3(5m - 2n + 3p)$

7 $6(4r - 3s - 2t)$ **8** $8(4r + 2s + t)$

9 $4(3u + 5v)$ **10** $6(4w + 3x)$

11 $2(5y + z)$ **12** $4(3y + 2z)$

13 $5(3v + 2)$ **14** $3(7 + 4w)$

15 $5(1 - 3a)$ **16** $3(8g - 5)$

EXERCISE 2.2H

Factorise these expressions fully.

1 $8x + 20$ **2** $3x + 6$ **3** $9x - 12$

4 $5x - 30$ **5** $16 + 8x$ **6** $9 + 15x$

7 $12 - 16x$ **8** $8 - 12x$ **9** $4x^2 + 16x$

10 $6x^2 + 30x$ **11** $8x^2 - 20x$ **12** $9x^2 - 15x$

STAG
6

Angles

EXERCISE 3.1H

1 Two of the angles of a triangle are 40°
and 75°.
What is the size of the third angle of the
triangle?

2 Find the size of each of the lettered angles
in these diagrams.

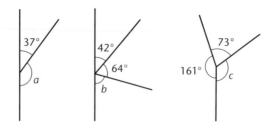

3 Find the size of each of the lettered angles
in this diagram.

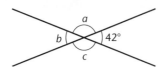

4 Look at these diagrams. Then copy and complete the table.

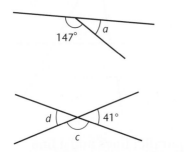 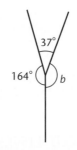

Angle	Size	Reason
a		Angles on a straight line add up to …°.
b		Angles at a … .
c		Angles … .
d		… angles at a point are … .

5 Three of the angles of a quadrilateral are 147°, 23° and 101°.
What is the size of the fourth angle of the quadrilateral?

▌▌▌ EXERCISE 3.2H

1 Find the value of *a*, *b*, and *c* in these diagrams, giving your reasons.

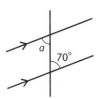 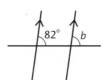 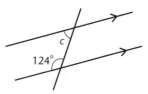

2 Find the size of d, e
and f in this diagram.

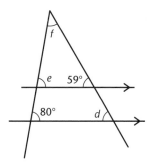

3 Draw accurately a pair of parallel lines and a line
crossing them.
Mark on your drawing a pair of alternate angles.

4 Find the size of each of the
lettered angles in this diagram.

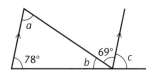

5 In a parallelogram ABCD, angle ABC is 49°.
Sketch the parallelogram and mark clearly the size of
each interior angle.

▌▌▌ EXERCISE 3.3H

Calculate the size of each of the angles marked with a
letter.

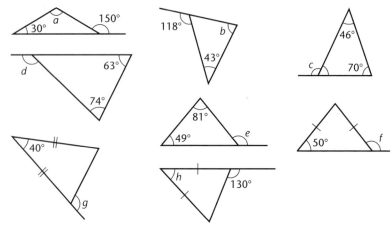

EXERCISE 3.4H

1 Three of the exterior angles of a quadrilateral are 125°, 68° and 95°.
Find the size of the other exterior angle.

2 Four of the exterior angles of a pentagon are 62°, 55°, 68° and 105°.
Find the size of the other exterior angle.

3 Four of the exterior angles of a hexagon are 72°, 45°, 68° and 81°.
The other two exterior angles are equal. Find the size of each of them.

4 Find the size of an interior angle of a regular octagon.
Show your working.

5 a) Calculate the sum of the interior angles of a pentagon.

   b) Four of the interior angles of a pentagon are 140°, 120°, 100° and 60°.
   Find the size of the other interior angle.

4 Probability

EXERCISE 4.1H

1 A shop has brown, white and wholemeal bread for sale.
The probability that someone will choose brown bread is 0·4 and the probability that they will choose white bread is 0·5.
What is the probability of someone choosing wholemeal bread?

2 Nina, Christine and Jean are the only entrants for the Mathematics prize.
The probability that Nina wins is 0·3 and the probability that Christine wins is 0·45.
What is the probability that Jean wins?

3 A bag contains red, white and blue counters.
John chooses a counter at random.
The probability that he chooses a red counter is 0·4 and the probability that he chooses a blue counter is 0·15.
What is the probability that he chooses a white counter?

4 At Millhouses Youth Club, members can choose to play table tennis, badminton or not to play anything.
The probability that Jake chooses table tennis is 0·65 and the probability that he chooses badminton is 0·25.
What is the probability that he chooses neither?

5 In a cricket match, the probability that Holbrook win is 0·23 and the probability that they lose is 0·47.
What is the probability that they draw?

6 Brian has a black, a green and a blue tie.
He decides to wear a tie.
The probability he selects the black tie is 0·28 and the probability he selects the green tie is 0·51.
What is the probability that he selects the blue tie?

7 In an experiment, four mutually exclusive outcomes are possible.
These are A, B, C and D.
$P(A) = 0·12$
$P(B) = 0·34$
$P(C) = 0·27$
Find $P(D)$.

8 A biased five-sided spinner is numbered 1 to 5.
The table shows the probability of obtaining some of the scores when it is spun.

Score	1	2	3	4	5
Probability	0·37	0·1	0·14		0·22

What is the probability of getting a 4?

STA
6

5 Translations

EXERCISE 5.1H pt

1 Copy the diagram.

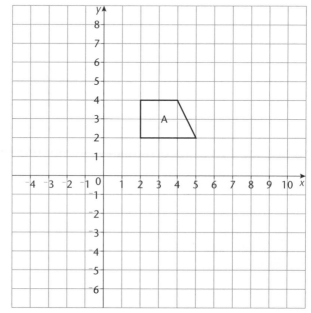

a) Translate shape A by $\begin{pmatrix} 0 \\ -6 \end{pmatrix}$.
Label the image B.

b) Translate shape A by $\begin{pmatrix} 4 \\ 3 \end{pmatrix}$.
Label the image C.

c) Translate shape A by $\begin{pmatrix} -6 \\ 4 \end{pmatrix}$.
Label the image D.

d) Translate shape A by $\begin{pmatrix} -4 \\ -7 \end{pmatrix}$.
Label the image E.

2 Draw a pair of axes and label them ⁻3 to 5 for x and y.
Draw a triangle with vertices at $(2, 1), (2, 3)$ and $(3, 1)$.
Label it A.

a) Translate triangle A by $\begin{pmatrix} 2 \\ 1 \end{pmatrix}$.
Label the image B.

b) Translate triangle A by $\begin{pmatrix} -5 \\ -3 \end{pmatrix}$.
Label the image C.

c) Translate triangle A by $\begin{pmatrix} 2 \\ -4 \end{pmatrix}$.
Label the image D.

3 Look at this diagram.

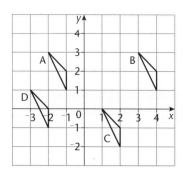

Describe the single transformation that maps

a) triangle A on to triangle B.

b) triangle A on to triangle C.

c) triangle A on to triangle D.

d) triangle B on to triangle D.

4 Look at this diagram.

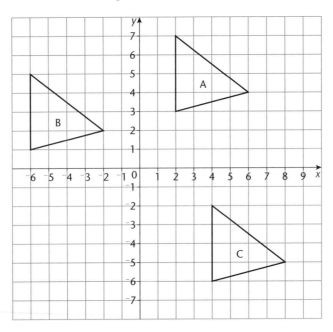

Describe the single transformation that maps

a) triangle A on to triangle B.

b) triangle A on to triangle C.

c) triangle B on to triangle C.

d) triangle C on to triangle B.

Fractions

EXERCISE 6.1H

1 For each pair of fractions
- find the lowest common denominator.
- state which is the bigger fraction.

a) $\frac{7}{8}$ or $\frac{3}{4}$ **b)** $\frac{5}{9}$ or $\frac{7}{11}$

c) $\frac{1}{6}$ or $\frac{3}{20}$ **d)** $\frac{2}{3}$ or $\frac{4}{5}$

e) $\frac{2}{7}$ or $\frac{3}{10}$ **f)** $\frac{5}{8}$ or $\frac{2}{3}$

2 Write each of these sets of fractions in order, smallest first.

a) $\frac{1}{2}$ $\frac{3}{8}$ $\frac{9}{16}$ $\frac{3}{4}$ $\frac{5}{16}$

b) $\frac{3}{4}$ $\frac{7}{12}$ $\frac{19}{36}$ $\frac{5}{6}$ $\frac{4}{9}$

EXERCISE 6.2H

1 Copy and complete these equivalent fractions.

$$\frac{2}{3} = \frac{6}{\square} = \frac{\square}{15} = \frac{24}{\square}$$

2 Write these fractions in their lowest terms.

a) $\frac{12}{16}$ **b)** $\frac{3}{30}$ **c)** $\frac{15}{40}$ **d)** $\frac{8}{20}$

For questions **3** to **7**, give your answers in their lowest terms.

3 Work out these.

a) $\frac{3}{7} + \frac{2}{7}$ **b)** $\frac{7}{15} + \frac{4}{15}$

c) $\frac{8}{11} - \frac{3}{11}$ **d)** $\frac{11}{17} - \frac{8}{17}$

e) $\frac{7}{16} + \frac{3}{16}$ **f)** $\frac{7}{9} + \frac{4}{9}$

g) $\frac{7}{12} - \frac{5}{12}$ **h)** $\frac{8}{11} + \frac{5}{11}$

4 Add these fractions.

a) $\frac{2}{9} + \frac{4}{9}$ **b)** $\frac{2}{5} + \frac{3}{10}$

c) $\frac{1}{4} + \frac{1}{5}$ **d)** $\frac{1}{3} + \frac{3}{10}$

e) $\frac{3}{8} + \frac{1}{6}$

5 Subtract these fractions.

a) $\frac{3}{8} - \frac{1}{8}$ **b)** $\frac{5}{8} - \frac{1}{4}$

c) $\frac{1}{3} - \frac{1}{8}$ **d)** $\frac{5}{6} - \frac{3}{8}$

e) $\frac{5}{8} - \frac{2}{5}$

6 Work out these.

a) $\frac{2}{9} + \frac{1}{3}$ **b)** $\frac{7}{12} + \frac{1}{4}$

c) $\frac{3}{4} - \frac{1}{10}$ **d)** $\frac{13}{16} - \frac{3}{8}$

e) $\frac{7}{8} + \frac{1}{3}$ **f)** $\frac{4}{5} + \frac{5}{6}$

g) $\frac{7}{12} - \frac{1}{8}$ **h)** $\frac{9}{20} + \frac{3}{4}$

i) $\frac{7}{11} + \frac{3}{5}$ **j)** $\frac{7}{12} + \frac{7}{10}$

k) $\frac{7}{8} - \frac{1}{6}$ **l)** $\frac{7}{15} - \frac{3}{20}$

7 Work out these.

a) $\frac{2}{5} + \frac{1}{4} - \frac{1}{2}$ **b)** $\frac{3}{8} + \frac{3}{4} - \frac{2}{3}$ **c)** $\frac{1}{3} + \frac{1}{4} + \frac{1}{5}$

EXERCISE 6.3H

1 Work out these.
Write your answers as simply as possible.

a) $2\frac{4}{7} + 3\frac{1}{7}$ $\qquad$ **b)** $4\frac{5}{6} - 1\frac{1}{6}$

c) $5\frac{9}{13} - \frac{4}{13}$ $\qquad$ **d)** $4\frac{3}{8} - 1\frac{5}{8}$

2 Add these fractions.
Write your answers as simply as possible.

a) $\frac{3}{4} + 1\frac{1}{2}$ $\qquad$ **b)** $1\frac{1}{4} + \frac{3}{5}$

c) $2\frac{1}{5} + 1\frac{3}{5}$ $\qquad$ **d)** $4\frac{1}{2} + 2\frac{3}{5}$

e) $1\frac{5}{6} + \frac{2}{5}$

3 Subtract these fractions.
Write your answers as simply as possible.

a) $2\frac{7}{8} - \frac{3}{8}$ $\qquad$ **b)** $3\frac{5}{6} - 1\frac{3}{8}$

c) $4\frac{1}{4} - 2\frac{1}{8}$ $\qquad$ **d)** $3\frac{1}{2} - \frac{3}{5}$

e) $6\frac{1}{10} - 4\frac{2}{5}$

4 Work out these.

a) $4\frac{1}{4} + 3\frac{1}{3}$ $\qquad$ **b)** $6\frac{8}{9} - 1\frac{2}{3}$

c) $5\frac{3}{8} + \frac{1}{4}$ $\qquad$ **d)** $5\frac{11}{16} - 2\frac{1}{8}$

e) $2\frac{5}{6} + 3\frac{1}{4}$ $\qquad$ **f)** $6\frac{8}{9} - 2\frac{1}{6}$

g) $3\frac{5}{8} + 4\frac{7}{10}$ $\qquad$ **h)** $5\frac{11}{16} - 5\frac{1}{3}$

i) $4\frac{3}{4} + 3\frac{2}{7}$ $\qquad$ **j)** $6\frac{1}{4} - 2\frac{2}{3}$

k) $7\frac{1}{9} - 2\frac{1}{2}$ $\qquad$ **l)** $5\frac{3}{10} - 4\frac{4}{5}$

Plans and elevations

EXERCISE 7.1H

Sketch the plan and elevations of each of the
solid shapes in questions **1** to **4**.
The arrows indicate the direction of the plan, P,
the front elevation, F, and the side elevation, S.

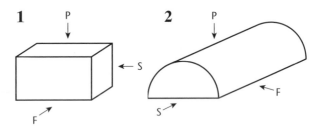

1   P   ←S   F

2   P   F   S

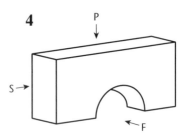

3   P   ←S   F

4   P   S→   ←F

Draw accurately the full-size plan and elevations of each of the solid shapes in questions **5** to **7**.
The arrows indicate the direction of the plan, P, the front elevation, F, and the side elevation, S.

5

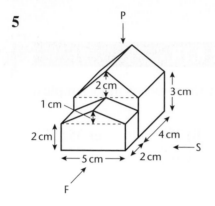

6

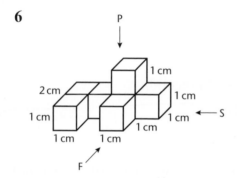

7

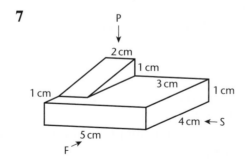

8 Ratio

TAGE

6

EXERCISE 8.1H

1 Write each of these ratios in its simplest form.

   a) $8:6$ **b)** $20:50$ **c)** $35:55$

   d) $8:24:32$ **e)** $15:25:20$

2 Write each of these ratios in its simplest form.

   a) 200 g : 500 g

   b) 60p : £3

   c) 1 minute : 25 seconds

   d) 2 m : 80 cm

   e) 500 g : 3 kg

3 A bar of brass contains 400 g of copper and 200 g of zinc.
   Write the ratio of copper to zinc in its simplest form.

4 Terry, Janine and Abigail receive £200, £350 and £450 respectively as their dividends in a joint investment.
   Write the ratio of their dividends in its simplest form.

5 Three saucepans hold 500 ml, 1 litre and 2·5 litres respectively.
   Write the ratio of their capacities in its simplest form.

EXERCISE 8.2H

1 Write each of these ratios in the form $1:n$.

  a) $2:10$ **b)** $5:30$ **c)** $2:9$

  d) $4:9$ **e)** $50\,g:30\,g$ **f)** $15p:£3$

  g) $25\,cm:6\,m$ **h)** $20:7$ **i)** $4\,cm:1\,km$

2 On a map a distance of 12 mm represents a distance of 3 km.
What is the scale of the map in the form $1:n$?

3 A picture is enlarged on a photocopier from 25 mm wide to 15 cm wide.
What is the ratio of the picture to the enlargement in the form $1:n$?

EXERCISE 8.3H

1 Concentrated orange and water are mixed in the ratio 1 to 5 to make squash.

  a) How much water should be mixed with 50 ml of concentrated orange?

  b) How much concentrated orange should be mixed with 1 litre (1000 ml) of water?

2 A photo is enlarged in the ratio $1:5$.

  a) The length of the small photo is 15 cm.
    What is the length of the large photo?

  b) The width of the large photo is 45 cm.
    What is the width of the small photo?

3 Two people share all their costs in the ratio 2 to 3.

  a) If the first pays £400, how much does the second pay?

  b) If the second pays £150, how much does the first pay?

4 To make pink paint, red and white paint are mixed in the ratio 3 parts red to 5 parts white.

   a) How much white is mixed with 15 litres of red?

   b) How much red is mixed with 350 ml of white?

5 The Michelin motoring atlas of France has a scale of 1 cm to 2 km.

   a) On the map the distance between Metz and Nancy is 25 cm.
   How far is the actual distance between the two towns?

   b) The actual distance between Caen and Falaise is 33 km.
   How far is this on the map?

6 Graham is making pastry.
To make enough for five people he uses 300 g of flour.
How much flour should he use for eight people?

7 To make a solution of a chemical a scientist mixes 2 parts chemical with 25 parts water.

   a) How much water should he mix with 10 ml of chemical?

   b) How much chemical should he mix with 1 litre of water?

8 The ratio of the sides of two similar rectangles is 2 : 5.

   a) The length of the small rectangle is 4 cm.
   How long is the big rectangle?

   b) The width of the big rectangle is 7·5 cm.
   How wide is the small rectangle?

EXERCISE 8.4H

Do not use your calculator for questions **1** to **8**.

1 Share £40 between Paula and Tom in the ratio 3 : 5.

2 Split £1950 in the ratio 4 : 5 : 6.

3 Nasim and Andrew share a bill in the ratio 2 : 3.
The bill is £21·00.
How much does Andrew pay?

4 Sue, Jane and Christine invest £70 000 between them in
the ratio 2 : 3 : 5.
How much do they each invest?

5 To make mortar, sand and cement are mixed in the
ratio 5 parts sand to 1 part cement.
How much of each is needed to make 12 kg of mortar?

6 Grey paint is made with 2 parts white to 3 parts black.
How much black is needed to make 2·5 litres of grey?

7 A metal alloy is made up of copper, iron and nickel in
the ratio 3 : 4 : 2.
How much of each metal is there in 450 g of the alloy?

8 Ian worked 6 hours one day.
The time he spent on filing, writing and computing was
in the ratio 2 : 3 : 7.
How long did he spend computing?

You may use a calculator for questions **9** and **10**.

9 Hollie spends her pocket money on sweets, magazines
and clothes in the ratio 2 : 3 : 7. She receives £15 a week.
How much does she spend on sweets?

10 In a questionnaire the three possible answers are 'Yes',
'No' and 'Don't know'.
The answers from a group of 456 people are in the
ratio 10 : 6 : 3.
How many 'Don't knows' are there?

9 Solving equations

EXERCISE 9.1H

Solve these equations.

1 $2x + 5 = 11$ **2** $3x - 1 = 14$

3 $6x + 3 = 27$ **4** $4x - 9 = 31$

5 $7x + 8 = 50$

EXERCISE 9.2H

Solve these equations.

1 $3(x - 2) = 18$ **2** $2(1 + x) = 8$

3 $3(x - 5) = 6$ **4** $2(x + 3) = 10$

5 $5(x - 2) = 15$ **6** $2(x - 3) = 6$

7 $5(x - 4) = 20$ **8** $4(x + 1) = 16$

9 $2(x - 7) = 8$ **10** $3(2x + 3) = 18$

11 $5(2x - 3) = 15$ **12** $2(3x - 2) = 14$

13 $5(2x - 3) = 40$ **14** $4(x - 3) = 6$

15 $2(2x - 3) = 8$

EXERCISE 9.3H

Solve these equations.

1 $5x - 1 = 3x + 5$ **2** $5x + 1 = 2x + 13$

3 $7x - 2 = 2x + 8$ **4** $6x + 1 = 4x + 21$

5 $9x - 10 = 4x + 5$ **6** $5x - 8 = 3x - 6$

7 $6x + 2 = 10 - 2x$ **8** $2x - 10 = 5 - 3x$

9 $15 + 3x = 2x + 18$ **10** $2x - 5 = 4 - x$

11 $3x - 2 = x + 7$ **12** $x - 1 = 2x - 6$

13 $2x - 4 = 2 - x$ **14** $9 - x = x + 5$

15 $3x - 2 = x - 8$

10 Powers and indices

Write these in a simpler form, using indices.

1 a) $7 \times 7 \times 7 \times 7 \times 7$

  b) $3 \times 3 \times 3 \times 3 \times 3$

  c) $2 \times 2 \times 2 \times 2 \times 2 \times 2$

  d) $5 \times 5 \times 5$

2 a) $d \times d \times d \times d \times d \times d \times d$

  b) $m \times m \times m \times m \times m \times m$

  c) $t \times t \times t \times t \times t \times t \times t$

  d) $a \times a \times a \times a$

3 a) $a \times a \times a \times a \times b \times b$

  b) $c \times c \times c \times c \times d \times d \times d \times d \times d$

  c) $r \times r \times r \times s \times s \times t \times t \times t \times t$

  d) $m \times m \times p \times p \times p \times t \times t$

4 a) $2x \times 3x \times 6x$

  b) $2a \times 3a \times a$

  c) $y \times 2y \times 3y$

  d) $5a \times 4a \times 2a \times a$

5 a) $5 \times 5 + 3 \times 3$

  b) $2 \times 2 \times 2 + 3 \times 3$

  c) $6 \times 6 - 2 \times 2$

  d) $7 \times 7 \times 7 - 5 \times 5 \times 5$

EXERCISE 10.2H

1 Calculate the value of y in each of these formulae by substituting the values of x given.

a) $y = 2x + 1$
    (i) $x = 2$ **(ii)** $x = {}^-2$

b) $y = 3x - 1$
    (i) $x = 2$ **(ii)** $x = {}^-2$

c) $y = x^2 - 1$
    (i) $x = 2$ **(ii)** $x = {}^-2$

d) $y = 2x^2 + x$
    (i) $x = 2$ **(ii)** $x = {}^-3$

e) $y = x^2 - 2x + 3$
    (i) $x = 4$ **(ii)** $x = {}^-2$

2 a) For the formula $A = b - c$,
    find A when $b = 6$ and $c = 3{\cdot}5$.

b) For the formula $B = 2a - b$,
    find B when $a = 6$ and $b = 5$.

c) For the formula $C = 2a - b + 3c$,
    find C when $a = 3{\cdot}5, b = 2{\cdot}6$ and $c = 1{\cdot}2$.

d) For the formula $D = 3b^2$,
    find D when $b = 2$.

e) For the formula $E = ab - cd$,
    find E when $a = 12{\cdot}5, b = 6, c = 3{\cdot}5$ and $d = 8$.

f) For the formula $F = \dfrac{a - b}{5}$,
    find F when $a = 6$ and $b = 3{\cdot}5$.

11 Circles

pt

1 Calculate the circumference of the circles with these diameters, giving your answers correct to 1 decimal place.

a) 8 cm   **b)** 17 cm   **c)** 39·2 cm

d) 116 mm   **e)** 5·1 m   **f)** 6·32 m

g) 14 cm   **h)** 23 cm

2 Find the circumference of circles with these radii, giving your answers correct to 1 decimal place.

a) 78 mm   **b)** 39 mm

c) 4·4 m   **d)** 2·75 m

EXERCISE 11.2H

1 Find the area of the circles with these radii.

a) 17 cm   **b)** 23 cm   **c)** 67 cm

d) 43 mm   **e)** 74 mm   **f)** 32 cm

g) 58 cm   **h)** 4·3 cm

2 Find the area of the circles with these diameters.

a) 18 cm   **b)** 28 cm   **c)** 68 cm

d) 38 mm   **e)** 78 mm   **f)** 58 cm

g) 46 cm   **h)** 6·4 cm

Scatter diagrams

12

You may find the example useful for both of these exercises.

Draw a scatter diagram for each of these sets of data.

1

x	y
4	20
5	21
8	36
9	28
15	40
12	31
13	35
16	40
7	30

2

x	y
19	9
21	6
10	12
14	10
17	6
16	7
13	8
12	9
10	15

STAG

6

EXERCISE 12.2H

1 Comment on the correlation, if any, between x and y in questions **1** and **2** of Exercise 12.1H.

2 These are the marks of 10 students in Class 10A in English and geography.

English	Geography
59	59
69	64
41	50
62	61
45	55
85	80
50	60
65	72
77	75
48	54

a) Draw a scatter diagram to show this information.

b) Comment on the correlation between the marks in the two subjects.

c) Draw a line of best fit.
   Use your line to estimate these.
   (i) The geography mark of a student who gained 60 marks in English
   (ii) The English mark of a student who gained 70 marks in geography

3 This table gives the average maximum temperature and the rainfall in June for 10 different cities.

Temperature (°C)	Rainfall (mm)
18	47
19	64
20	60
21	73
22	84
23	37
24	49
27	29
28	63
29	47

a) Draw a scatter diagram to show this information.

b) Comment on the correlation, if any, between the temperature and the rainfall.

c) Another city has an average maximum temperature of 23°C in June.
What can you deduce from the scatter diagram about its average rainfall?

STA

1 Make two copies of this diagram and answer each part of the question on a separate diagram.

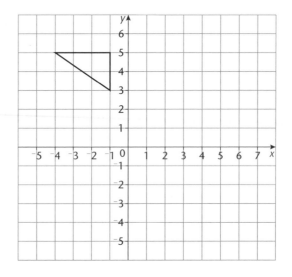

a) Rotate the triangle through 90° clockwise about the origin.

b) Rotate the triangle through 180° about the origin.

2 Make two copies of this diagram and answer each part of the question on a separate diagram.

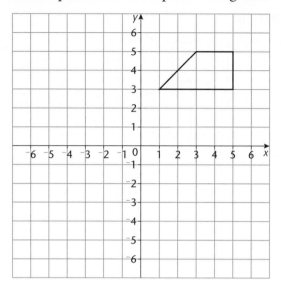

a) Rotate the quadrilateral through 90° clockwise about the origin.

b) Rotate the quadrilateral through 90° anticlockwise about the origin.

3 Make two copies of this diagram and answer each part of the question on a separate diagram.

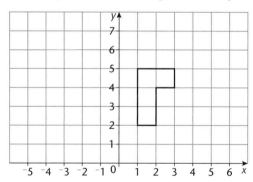

a) Rotate the shape through 180° about the point $(3, 4)$.

b) Rotate the shape through 90° anticlockwise about the point $(1, 2)$.

1 Copy the diagram.

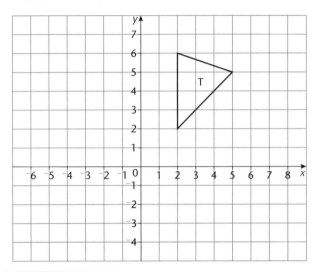

a) Rotate triangle T through 90° anticlockwise about the point (5, 5). Label the image A.

b) Describe the transformation that maps triangle A on to triangle T.

c) On the same diagram, rotate triangle T through 180° about the point (0, 3). Label the image B.

d) Describe the transformation that maps triangle B on to triangle T.

2 Copy the diagram.

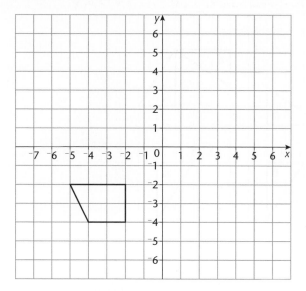

a) Rotate the shape through 90° anticlockwise about the point (⁻5, ⁻2). Label the image A.

b) On the same diagram, rotate the original shape through 90° clockwise about the point (0, ⁻1). Label the image B.

c) Describe fully the single transformation that maps A on to B.

STA

3 Look at this diagram.

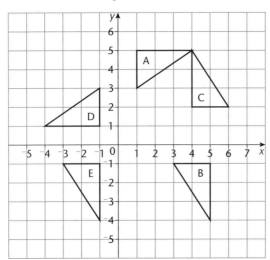

Describe fully the single transformation that maps

a) A on to B.

b) A on to C.

c) A on to D.

d) D on to E.

Multilplying and dividing fractions

||| EXERCISE 14.1H   pt

Work out these. Where necessary, write your answers as proper fractions or mixed numbers in their lowest terms.

1 $\frac{3}{7} \times 5$

2 $\frac{5}{9} \times 6$

3 $\frac{3}{5} \div 4$

4 $6 \times \frac{5}{11}$

5 $\frac{2}{9} \div 4$

6 $9 \div \frac{3}{8}$

7 $\frac{1}{4} \times \frac{3}{5}$

8 $\frac{1}{5} \times \frac{1}{4}$

9 $\frac{3}{4} \times \frac{2}{3}$

10 $\frac{4}{5} \times \frac{1}{2}$

11 $\frac{3}{4} \times \frac{8}{9}$

12 $\frac{5}{6} \times \frac{3}{5}$

13 $\frac{1}{4} \div \frac{3}{5}$

14 $\frac{4}{5} \div \frac{3}{5}$

15 $\frac{2}{3} \times \frac{5}{7}$

16 $\frac{1}{8} \times \frac{5}{6}$

17 $\frac{7}{9} \times \frac{2}{5}$

18 $\frac{5}{8} \div \frac{3}{4}$

19 $\frac{3}{8} \div \frac{1}{3}$

20 $\frac{4}{9} \times \frac{5}{11}$

21 $\frac{6}{7} \times \frac{1}{8}$

22 $\frac{7}{15} \div \frac{2}{3}$

23 $\frac{7}{12} \times \frac{3}{8}$

24 $\frac{9}{16} \div \frac{7}{12}$

25 $\frac{7}{10} \div \frac{5}{12}$

26 $\frac{7}{30} \times \frac{10}{21}$

15 Decimals

TAGE
6

EXERCISE 15.1H

1 Work out these.

a) £4·37 + £5·23

b) £2·61 + £3·42

c) £8·46 + £5·79

d) £5·83 − £2·54

e) £6·23 + £3·74 − £4·66

2 Work out these.

a) $\begin{array}{r} 3\cdot87 \\ + 9\cdot15 \\ \hline \end{array}$ **b)** $\begin{array}{r} 38\cdot43 \\ + 59\cdot12 \\ \hline \end{array}$ **c)** $\begin{array}{r} 41\cdot53 \\ + 67\cdot42 \\ \hline \end{array}$

3 Work out these.

a) $\begin{array}{r} 19\cdot28 \\ - 6\cdot25 \\ \hline \end{array}$ **b)** $\begin{array}{r} 47\cdot16 \\ - 15\cdot42 \\ \hline \end{array}$ **c)** $\begin{array}{r} 253\cdot80 \\ - 81\cdot47 \\ \hline \end{array}$

4 Work out these.

a) £3·95 + 82p + £1·57

b) £15·21 + 77p + £3·42 + 61p

c) £63·84 + 90p + £8·51 + £91·20 + 47p

d) £6·25 + 42p + 87p + £63·20

5 In the javelin, Amina throws 52·15 m and Raj throws 46·47 m.
Find the difference between the lengths of their throws.

6 The times for the first and last places in a show-jumping event were 47·82 seconds and 53·19 seconds. Find the difference between these times.

7 Holly buys two scarves at £8·45 each and a pair of shoes at £35·99.
How much change does she get from £60?

EXERCISE 15.2H

Work out these.

1 a) 4·1 × 10   **b)** 5·27 × 100

    c) 32·6 × 100   **d)** 0·125 × 1000

2 a) 21·4 ÷ 10   **b)** 172·5 ÷ 100

    c) 62·3 ÷ 100   **d)** 5·14 ÷ 1000

3 a) 1·72 × 10   **b)** 9·93 × 100

    c) 19·5 × 1000   **d)** 0·287 × 100

4 a) 16·2 ÷ 10   **b)** 584·7 ÷ 100

    c) 18·3 ÷ 100   **d)** 6·41 ÷ 1000

STA

Decimals

pt

1 Work out these.

   a) $1{\cdot}2 \times 4$ **b)** $2{\cdot}3 \times 0{\cdot}5$

   c) $4{\cdot}6 \times 200$ **d)** $2{\cdot}5 \times 1{\cdot}2$

   e) $1{\cdot}4 \times 0{\cdot}02$

2 Given that $47 \times 53 = 2491$ write down the answers to these.

   a) $4{\cdot}7 \times 5{\cdot}3$ **b)** $4{\cdot}7 \times 5300$

   c) $4{\cdot}7 \times 0{\cdot}053$ **d)** $0{\cdot}47 \times 5{\cdot}3$

   e) 47×5300

3 Work out these.

   a) $6 \times 0{\cdot}4$ **b)** $0{\cdot}2 \times 7$

   c) $5 \times 0{\cdot}3$ **d)** $0{\cdot}8 \times 9$

   e) $0{\cdot}4 \times 0{\cdot}1$ **f)** $0{\cdot}7 \times 0{\cdot}8$

   g) $50 \times 0{\cdot}7$ **h)** $0{\cdot}3 \times 80$

   i) $0{\cdot}4 \times 0{\cdot}3$ **j)** $0{\cdot}6 \times 0{\cdot}1$

   k) $(0{\cdot}7)^2$ **l)** $(0{\cdot}2)^2$

4 Work out these.

   a) $3{\cdot}6 \times 1{\cdot}4$ **b)** $5{\cdot}8 \times 2{\cdot}6$

   c) $8{\cdot}1 \times 4{\cdot}3$ **d)** $6{\cdot}5 \times 3{\cdot}2$

   e) $74 \times 1{\cdot}7$ **f)** $64 \times 3{\cdot}8$

5 Find the cost of six DVDs at £13·45 each.

6 Melissa buys three of these bags of carrots.

WEIGHT	PRICE
0.450 KG	99p

a) What is the total weight?

b) What is the total cost?

7 Find the cost of 3 kg of onions at £0·72 per kilogram.

8 Dean buys two newspapers at 55p each and three magazines at £1·20 each.
How much change does he get from £10?

EXERCISE 15.4H

1 Work out these.

   a) 20·5 ÷ 5   **b)** 36·2 ÷ 2

   c) 12·4 ÷ 4   **d)** 124·2 ÷ 3

   e) 5·45 ÷ 5

2 Work out these.

   a) 18·2 ÷ 5   **b)** 16·87 ÷ 2

   c) 9·3 ÷ 4   **d)** 43·92 ÷ 3

   e) 112·91 ÷ 7

3 Use division to convert these fractions to decimals.

   a) $\frac{2}{5}$ **b)** $\frac{3}{8}$ **c)** $\frac{9}{12}$

   d) $\frac{13}{20}$ **e)** $\frac{7}{40}$

STA

4 Change each of these fractions to a decimal.
  If necessary, give your answer to 3 decimal places.

a) $\frac{7}{8}$ b) $\frac{7}{100}$ c) $\frac{5}{9}$ d) $\frac{2}{11}$

EXERCISE 15.5H

Work out these.

1 a) $6 \div 0.3$ **b)** $4.8 \div 0.2$

 c) $2.4 \div 0.6$ **d)** $7.2 \div 0.4$

 e) $33 \div 1.1$ **f)** $60 \div 1.5$

 g) $12 \div 0.4$ **h)** $35 \div 0.7$

 i) $64 \div 0.8$ **j)** $32 \div 0.2$

 k) $2.17 \div 0.7$ **l)** $47.5 \div 0.5$

2 a) $23.6 \div 0.4$ **b)** $23.4 \div 0.8$

 c) $18.2 \div 0.7$ **d)** $31.2 \div 0.6$

 e) $42.3 \div 0.9$ **f)** $75.6 \div 1.2$

 g) $5.28 \div 0.3$ **h)** $7.56 \div 0.7$

 i) $63.2 \div 0.2$ **j)** $6.27 \div 1.1$

 k) $3.51 \div 1.3$ **l)** $8.19 \div 1.3$

Linear graphs

EXERCISE 16.1H

1 On a grid, draw and label axes from $^-5$ to 5 for both x and y.
Then draw and label the line for each of these equations.

$$x = {}^-4, \quad x = 2, \quad y = 4, \quad y = {}^-3$$

2 Draw the graph of $y = 2x$, for $x = {}^-3$ to 3.

3 Draw the graph of $y = 2x + 3$, for $x = {}^-3$ to 3.

4 Draw the graph of $y = 3x - 2$, for $x = {}^-2$ to 4.

5 Draw the graph of $y = 6 - 2x$, for $x = {}^-2$ to 4.

STAG

6

EXERCISE 16.2H (pt)

1 Draw the graph of $x + y = 10$.

2 Draw the graph of $x + 2y = 10$.

3 Draw the graph of $3x + 4y = 12$.

4 Draw the graph of $2x + 6y = 12$.

5 Draw the graph of $2y = 3x - 4$ for $x = {}^-2$ to 4.

Real-life graphs

pt

1 This graph shows Michael's journey from Dorton to Canburn on a bicycle.

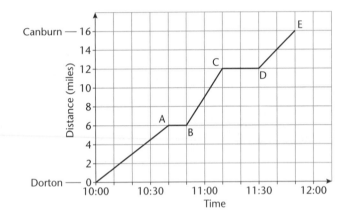

a) Which parts of the graph show Michael not moving?

b) What time did Michael get to Canburn?

c) How far did he travel altogether?

TAGE

6

2 John and Imran live in the same block of flats and go to the same school.
The graph represents their journeys home from school.

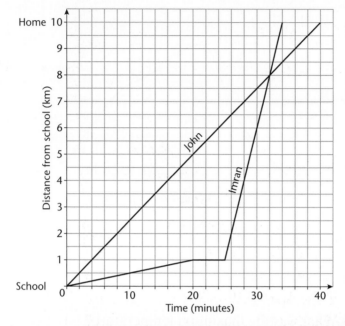

a) Describe Imran's journey home.

b) After how many minutes did Imran overtake John?

c) How many minutes before John did Imran arrive home?

d) Calculate John's speed in kilometres per minute.

3 The graph shows the temperature on a certain day.

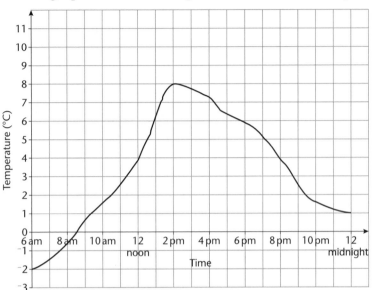

a) At what time did the temperature first go above freezing point (0°C)?

b) What was the maximum temperature?

c) At what time was the temperature rising most quickly?

d) For how many hours was the temperature above 6°C?

4 A model plane was launched.
It rose to a height of 25 metres in 30 seconds.
It climbed slowly at first and then faster.
It flew at a height of about 25 metres for 60 seconds.
It then dived to the ground in 5 seconds.

Draw a sketch graph to illustrate this story.

Drawing triangles and other shapes

18

1 a) Draw this triangle accurately.

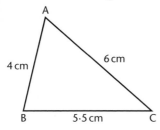

b) Measure angle A.

2 a) Draw this triangle accurately.

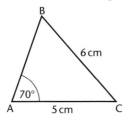

b) Measure the length of AB.

3 a) Draw this triangle accurately.

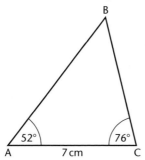

b) Measure the length of BC.

STAGE
6

4 a) Draw this triangle accurately.

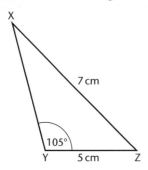

b) Measure angle YXZ.

5 AC is the shorter diagonal of a kite.
The length of AC is 4·6 cm.
The sides AB and BC are each 5·8 cm and the sides
AD and CD are each 8·3 cm.

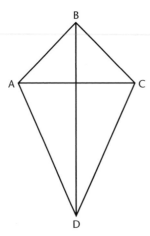

a) Draw the kite accurately.

b) Measure the length of diagonal BD.

EXERCISE 18.2H

1 Draw a circle of radius 5 cm.
Construct a regular pentagon with vertices on the circle.

Using a pen or coloured pencil, join the vertices of the pentagon that are not next to each other, to make a five-pointed star like this.

EXERCISE 18.3H

1 Which of these shapes will fold to make a cube?

a) 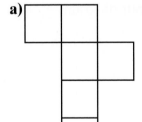 b) 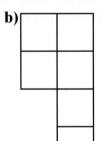 c)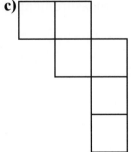

d) 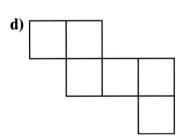 e)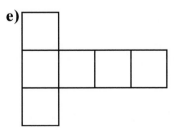

STA

2 On squared paper, draw a net for this cuboid.
The lengths are given in centimetres.

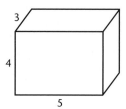

3 Construct an accurate net for a regular tetrahedron
of side 4 cm.

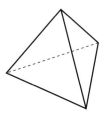

4 A pyramid has a square base of side 14 cm and sloping
edges each of length 12 cm.
Sketch a net for this pyramid, showing the
measurements of each line on your diagram.

AGE

Area and perimeter

19

You may find the example useful for Exercises 19.1H and 19.4H.

EXERCISE 19.1H

1 Find the area of each of these triangles. All lengths are in centimetres.

a)
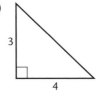

b)

c)
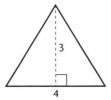

d)

e)
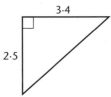

f)
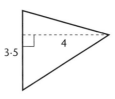

g)
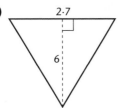

h)
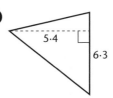

STAG
6

51

2 A triangle has vertices at $(1, 2)$, $(2, 5)$ and $(8, 2)$.
Draw the triangle on squared paper and find its area.

EXERCISE 19.2H

1 Find the area of each of these parallelograms.
All lengths are in centimetres.

a)

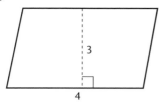

3

4

b)

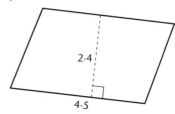

2·4

4·5

c)

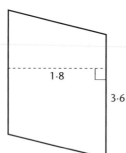

1·8

3·6

d)

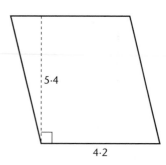

5·4

4·2

2 Find the lengths x, y, and z.

a)

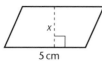

x

5 cm

Area = 20 cm²

b)

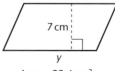

7 cm

y

Area = 22·4 cm²

c)

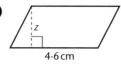

z

4·6 cm

Area = 16·1 cm²

EXERCISE 19.3H

1 Find the area of each of these trapezia.
All lengths are in centimetres.

a)

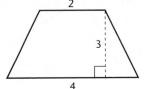

b)

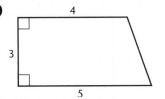

c)

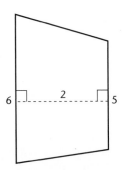

d)

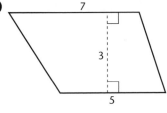

2 Find the lengths x and y.

a)

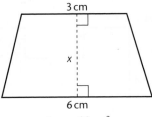

Area = 18 cm²

b)

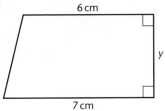

Area = 32·5 cm²

STA

▮▮▮ EXERCISE 19.4H

1 Find the perimeter of each of these shapes.
All lengths are in centimetres.

a)
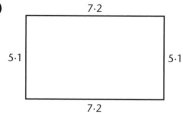

b)
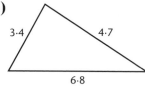

c)
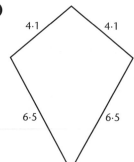

2 Here are the floor plans of some rooms. All the lengths
are in metres. For each room, work out
(i) its perimeter. **(ii)** its area.

a)
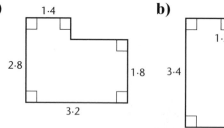

b)
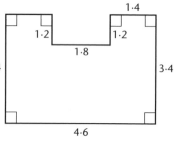

c)
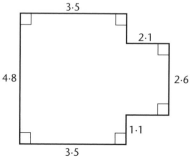

3 Work out the area of each of these shapes.

a)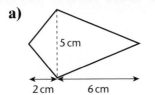

b)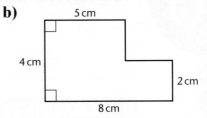

c)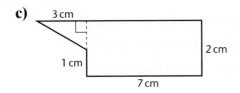

4 a) On squared paper, plot the points A(1, 3), B(6, 0), C(8, 5) and D(2, 7).
Join them to make a quadrilateral ABCD.

b) Split the shape into triangles and rectangles and find its area.

5 a) On squared paper, plot the points A(3, 9), B(6, 7), C(7, 3), D(3, 1) and E(0, 2).
Join them to make a pentagon ABCDE.

b) Split the pentagon into triangles and rectangles and find its area.

STA

Volume and surface area

EXERCISE 20.1H

1 The edges of a cube are 5 cm long.

  a) Calculate the volume of the cube.

  b) Calculate the surface area of the cube.

2 A box is 10 cm high, 5 cm long and 3 cm wide.

  a) Calculate the volume of the box.

  b) Calculate the surface area of the box.

3 A classroom is 6 metres long, 4 metres wide and 3 metres high.

  a) Calculate its volume.

  b) Calculate the surface area of the walls.

4 A biscuit tin is 12 cm long, 5 cm wide and 6 cm deep and has a lid.

  a) Calculate its volume.

  b) Calculate the surface area of the tin.

5 a) Calculate the volume of each of these cuboids. All lengths are in centimetres.

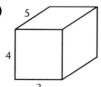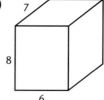

  (i) 5, 4, 3

  (ii) 7, 8, 6

  b) Calculate the total surface area of each of the cuboids.

6 This is a sketch of the net for a regular tetrahedron (triangular-based pyramid).

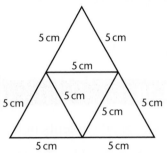

5 cm   5 cm
5 cm
5 cm   5 cm
5 cm
5 cm
5 cm   5 cm

Construct the net accurately.
Take measurements from your drawing and hence calculate the surface area of the tetrahedron.

EXERCISE 20.2H

Find the volume of each of these shapes.

1

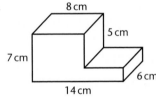

8 cm
5 cm
7 cm
6 cm
14 cm

2

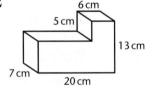

6 cm
5 cm
13 cm
7 cm
20 cm

3

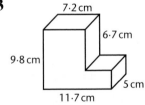

7·2 cm
6·7 cm
9·8 cm
5 cm
11·7 cm

4

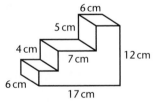

6 cm
5 cm
4 cm
7 cm
12 cm
6 cm
17 cm

5

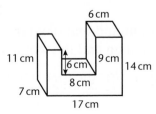

6 cm
11 cm
6 cm   9 cm
14 cm
8 cm
7 cm
17 cm

6

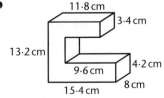

11·8 cm
3·4 cm
13·2 cm
4·2 cm
9·6 cm
15·4 cm
8 cm

Organising data

1 These are the marks of 30 students in a test.

32	42	23	37	28	12	37	6	5	37
17	18	31	29	27	11	21	37	28	37
22	31	23	47	23	12	24	34	41	43

a) Make a stem-and-leaf diagram of these marks.

b) Use your diagram to find

   (i) the median mark.

   (ii) the mode.

2 The ages of the first 25 men and the first 25 women to enter a supermarket on a Wednesday were recorded.

Men:

52	62	73	37	69	62	77	76	65
47	47	48	61	39	27	51	21	47
58	57	61	74	82	81	64

Women:

62	61	63	37	23	52	44	64	51
53	52	42	33	77	49	41	84	82
71	64	40	67	61	52	54

a) Make separate stem-and-leaf diagrams for the ages of the men and the women.

b) Find the median age for the men and for the women.

3 As part of a survey, Emma measured the heights, in centimetres, of the 50 teachers in her school.

Here are her results.

168	194	156	167	177	180	188	172	170
169	174	178	186	174	166	165	159	173
185	162	163	174	180	184	173	182	161
176	170	169	178	175	172	179	173	162
177	176	184	191	181	165	163	185	178
175	182	164	179	168				

Construct a stem-and-leaf diagram to show these heights.

EXERCISE 21.2H

1 For each of these sets of data

  (i) find the mode.

  (ii) find the range.

  (iii) calculate the mean.

a)

Number	Frequency
1	3
2	2
3	4
4	5
5	7
6	2
7	0
8	1
9	0
10	1

STA

b)

Number of drawing pins in a box	Number of boxes
98	5
99	14
100	36
101	28
102	17
103	13
104	7

c)

Number of snacks per day	Frequency
0	23
1	68
2	39
3	21
4	10
5	3
6	1

d)

Number of letters received on Monday	Frequency
0	19
1	37
2	18
3	24
4	12
5	5
6	2
7	3

2 Gift tokens cost £1, £5, £10, £20 or £50 each.
This frequency table shows the numbers of each value
of gift token sold in one bookstore on a Saturday.

Price of gift token (£)	Number of tokens sold
1	12
5	34
10	26
20	9
50	1

Calculate the mean value of gift token bought in the
bookstore that Saturday.

3 A sample of people were asked how many visits to the
cinema they had made in one month.
None of those asked had made more than eight visits
to the cinema.
This table shows the data.

Number of visits	Frequency
0	136
1	123
2	72
3	41
4	18
5	0
6	5
7	1
8	4

Calculate the mean number of visits to the cinema.

STA
6

EXERCISE 21.3H

1 The manager of a leisure centre recorded the weights of 120 men. Here are his results.

Weight (w kg)	Frequency
$60 \leqslant w < 65$	4
$65 \leqslant w < 70$	18
$70 \leqslant w < 75$	36
$75 \leqslant w < 80$	50
$80 \leqslant w < 85$	10
$85 \leqslant w < 90$	2

a) Draw a bar graph to represent these data.

b) Which of the intervals is the modal group?

c) Which of the intervals contains the median value?

2 This frequency diagram represents the times taken by a group of girls to run a race.

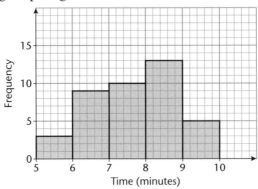

a) How many girls took longer than 9 minutes?

b) How many girls took part in the race?

c) What percentage of the girls took less than 7 minutes?

d) What is the most common finishing time?

e) Use the diagram to draw up a grouped frequency table like that in question **1**.

3 This table shows the heights of 40 plants.

Height (h cm)	Frequency
$3 \leqslant h < 4$	1
$4 \leqslant h < 5$	7
$5 \leqslant h < 6$	10
$6 \leqslant h < 7$	12
$7 \leqslant h < 8$	8
$8 \leqslant h < 9$	2

Draw a frequency polygon to represent these data.

4 This table shows the time taken for a group of children to get from home to school.

Time (t minutes)	Frequency
$0 \leqslant t < 5$	3
$5 \leqslant t < 10$	15
$10 \leqslant t < 15$	27
$15 \leqslant t < 20$	34
$20 \leqslant t < 25$	19
$25 \leqslant t < 30$	2

Draw a frequency polygon to represent these data.

STA

6

Enlargement

Use squared paper to answer questions **1** to **3**. In each case, copy the original diagram.

1 Make a '2 times' enlargement of this shape.

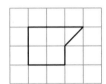

2 Enlarge this shape by scale factor 3 from the origin.

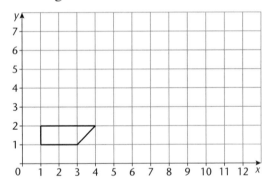

3 Enlarge this shape by scale factor 2 from the centre, O.

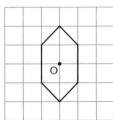

4 Work out the scale factor of enlargement of each of these pairs of shapes.

a)

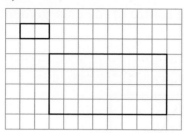

b)

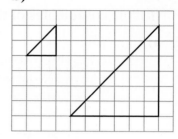

c)

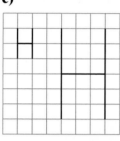

d)

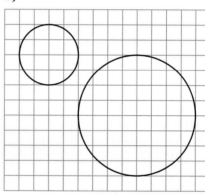

5 For each of these pairs of shapes, is the larger shape an enlargement of the smaller shape?
Give a reason for your answer.

a)

b)

STA

6 Copy each of these diagrams on to squared paper.
   For each of these diagrams find

   (i) the scale factor of the enlargement.

   (ii) the coordinates of the centre of the enlargement.

a)

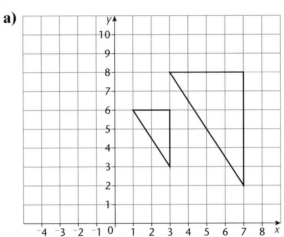

b)

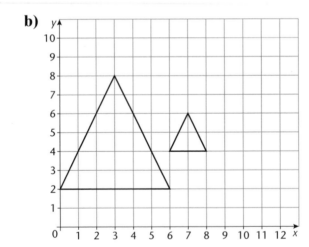

7 Describe fully the transformation that maps triangle A on to triangle B.

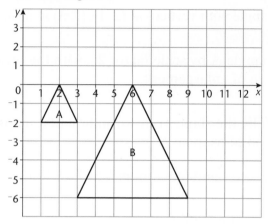

▌▌▌ EXERCISE 22.2H

1 Draw a pair of axes and label them 0 to 6 for both
x and *y*.

a) Draw a triangle with vertices at $(0, 6), (3, 6)$ and $(3, 3)$.
Label it A.

b) Enlarge triangle A by scale factor $\frac{1}{3}$, with the origin
as the centre of enlargement.
Label it B.

c) Describe fully the single transformation that maps
triangle B on to triangle A.

2 Draw a pair of axes and label them 0 to 6 for both
x and *y*.

a) Draw a triangle with vertices at $(5, 2), (5, 6)$ and $(3, 6)$.
Label it A.

b) Enlarge triangle A by scale factor $\frac{1}{2}$, with centre of
enlargement $(3, 2)$.
Label it B.

c) Describe fully the single transformation that maps
triangle B on to triangle A.

3 Draw a pair of axes and label them 0 to 8 for both x and y.

a) Draw a triangle with vertices at $(2, 1)$, $(2, 3)$ and $(3, 2)$. Label it A.

b) Enlarge triangle A by scale factor $2\frac{1}{2}$, with the origin as the centre of enlargement.
Label it B.

c) Describe fully the single transformation that maps triangle B on to triangle A.

4 Draw a pair of axes and label them 0 to 7 for both x and y.

a) Draw a trapezium with vertices at $(1, 2)$, $(1, 3)$, $(2, 3)$ and $(3, 2)$.
Label it A.

b) Enlarge trapezium A by scale factor 3, with centre of enlargement $(1, 2)$. Label the image B.

c) Describe fully the single transformation that maps trapezium B on to trapezium A.

5 Look at this diagram.

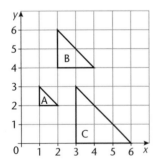

Describe fully the single transformation that maps

a) triangle A on to triangle B.

b) triangle B on to triangle A.

c) triangle A on to triangle C.

d) triangle C on to triangle A.

Transformations 23

You may find the example useful for both of these exercises.

EXERCISE 23.1H

1 Draw a pair of axes and label them ⁻2 to 4 for x and y.

  a) Draw a triangle with vertices at $(1, 1)$, $(1, 3)$ and $(0, 3)$.
  Label it A.

  b) Reflect triangle A in the line $x = 2$.
  Label the image B.

  c) Reflect triangle A in the line $y = x$.
  Label the image C.

  d) Reflect triangle A in the line $y = 2$.
  Label the image D.

2 Draw a pair of axes and label them ⁻3 to 3 for x and y.

  a) Draw a triangle with vertices at $(⁻1, 1)$, $(⁻1, 3)$ and $(⁻2, 3)$. Label it A.

  b) Reflect triangle A in the line $x = \frac{1}{2}$.
  Label the image B.

  c) Reflect triangle A in the line $y = x$.
  Label the image C.

  d) Reflect triangle A in the line $y = ⁻x$.
  Label the image D.

3 For each part

    (i) copy the diagram, making it larger if you wish.

    (ii) reflect the shape in the mirror line.

a)

b)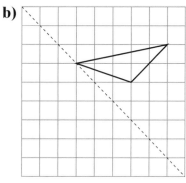

c)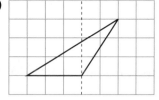

4 Look at this diagram.

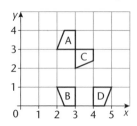

Describe fully the single transformation that maps

a) shape A on to shape B.

b) shape A on to shape C.

c) shape B on to shape D.

5 Look at this diagram.

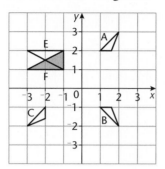

Describe fully the single transformation that maps

a) triangle A on to triangle B.

b) triangle A on to triangle C.

c) triangle E on to triangle F.

EXERCISE 23.2H

1 Copy the diagram.

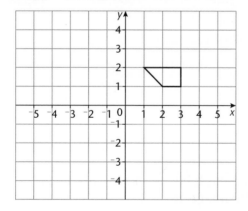

Rotate the shape through 90° anticlockwise about the origin.

2 Copy the diagram.

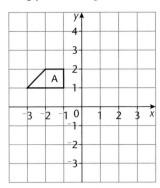

a) Rotate trapezium A through 180° about the origin. Label the image B.

b) Rotate trapezium A through 90° clockwise about the point (0, 1). Label the image C.

c) Rotate trapezium A through 90° anticlockwise about the point (⁻1, 1). Label the image D.

3 Copy the diagram.

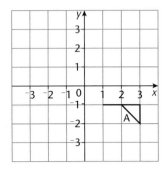

a) Rotate flag A through 90° clockwise about the origin. Label the image B.

b) Rotate flag A through 90° anticlockwise about the point (1, ⁻1). Label the image C.

c) Rotate flag A through 180° about the point (0, ⁻1). Label the image D.

4 Look at the diagram.

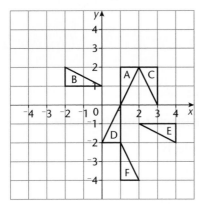

Describe fully the single transformation that maps

a) trapezium A on to trapezium B.

b) trapezium A on to trapezium C.

c) trapezium A on to trapezium D.

5 Look at the diagram.

Describe fully the single transformation that maps

a) triangle A on to triangle B.

b) triangle A on to triangle C.

c) triangle A on to triangle D.

d) triangle A on to triangle E.

e) triangle A on to triangle F.

> **Hint:** Some of these transformations are reflections.

6 Draw a pair of axes and label them ⁻2 to 6 for x and y.

a) Draw a triangle with vertices at $(1, 1), (1, 2)$ and $(4, 1)$. Label it A.

b) Translate triangle A by $\begin{pmatrix} 1 \\ 3 \end{pmatrix}$.

Label the image B.

c) Translate triangle A by $\begin{pmatrix} -3 \\ 4 \end{pmatrix}$.

Label the image C.

d) Translate triangle A by $\begin{pmatrix} -2 \\ -3 \end{pmatrix}$.

Label the image D.

7 Look at the diagram.

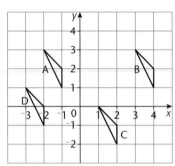

Describe the single transformation that maps

a) triangle A on to triangle B.

b) triangle A on to triangle C.

c) triangle A on to triangle D.

d) triangle B on to triangle D.

AGE
5

8 Look at the diagram.

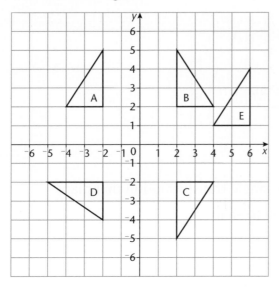

Describe the single transformation that maps

a) shape A on to shape B.

b) shape A on to shape C.

c) shape A on to shape D.

d) shape A on to shape E.

STA

6

9 Look at the diagram.

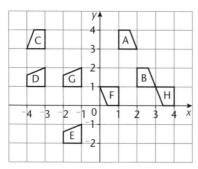

Describe the single transformation that maps

a) shape A on to shape B.

b) shape A on to shape C.

c) shape A on to shape D.

d) shape D on to shape E.

e) shape A on to shape F.

f) shape E on to shape G.

g) shape B on to shape H.

h) shape H on to shape F.

Hint: Not all the transformations are translations.

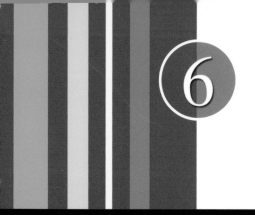

HOMEWORK BOOK
GRADUATED ASSESSMENT

This second edition of **Graduated Assessment for OCR** provides ideal preparation for the two-tier GCSE examination.

Each Book provides complete coverage of either one or two of the ten stages that make up the Graduated Assessment specification. Students use the combination of stages best suited to their needs and abilities, and the course can be further tailored to the requirements of each student.

This course, published especially for Graduated Assessment, has been written by experienced examiners and authors. It combines their teaching and examining experience to provide the ideal course for GCSE students.

This Homework Book gives students a parallel homework exercise for each exercise in the Student's Book, providing a range of questions that will be ideal preparation for the Foundation Tier examination. Each exercise is linked to the Stage 6 Student's Book, saving teachers valuable preparation time.

- Endorsed by OCR for use with the Two-Tier Modular Specification
- Ready-made homework
- Plenty of extra practice questions
- Dedicated student books, teacher's resources, homework books and digital resources
- Written by authors who are experienced teachers and examiners

This book covers Stage 6, which is a later stage of the Foundation Tier and the first stage of the Higher Tier.

ISBN 978-0-340-92755-7

9 780340 927557

Approved publication
OCR
RECOGNISING ACHIEVEMENT

Hodder Murray
www.hoddereducation.co.uk